Twinkle Twinkle Cricket Ball

HarperCollins*Children's Books*

First published in India in 2022 by **HarperCollins Children's Books**
An imprint of HarperCollins *Publishers*
Building No 10, Tower A, 4th Floor,
DLF Cyber City, Phase II, Gurugram 122002
www.harpercollins.co.in

2 4 6 8 10 9 7 5 3 1

P-ISBN: 9789356293748
E-ISBN: 9789356293755

Typeset in CookieRunOTF 14 pt/24 by **Shamika Chaves**

Printed and bound by Nutech Print Services – India

HarperCollinsIn

Ricky

MUHAHAHA! You may know Pang as the group leader, but the true leader is me! You'll understand if you stick around! HAHAHA!

Oliver

What great weather we have today.
On a day like this, I just want to sit by the lake, eat cookies, and listen to some music.
So... Please don't take my cookies!

Shasha

I can make anything I put my mind to! So tell me what you need.
But don't go asking for too much, okay?

PANG

I like anything fun! Join me if you are feeling down.
PANG! A game of cricket will help you feel better!

Cash

Let's go play right now!!
It'll be fun! Quickly!
Cash has lots of great ideas!

The sun was setting so an exciting game of cricket had to come to an end.

"We can't see the ball when it gets dark, so let's play again tomorrow,"
said Shasha.

Back at home,

Pang was sad that he couldn't continue the game.

Pang stood in front of the window,
looking up at the stars.

**"I wish we could play cricket
at night as well!"**
wished Pang.

That night Pang dreamed of a glowing ball
that shone brightly even at night.

In his dream, everyone enjoyed a fun game of cricket even when the sun was down.

The next day Pang visited Shasha with a great idea.
Pang asked Shasha to make
a twinkling ball that glowed in the dark.

"It will be quite difficult to make, but let's give it a try!"
said Shasha.

While helping Shasha,
Pang dropped a jar full of gold powder.

Poof!

The gold powder filled the room.

The only place they could find
more golden rocks was in the caves.

"We'll go and find more golden rocks!"
said Pang, Oliver, Ricky, and Cash.

The cave was very dark and scary.
Pang and Ricky were hiding behind Oliver when
Cash played a prank on his friends.

Boo!

Cash shouted.

Aaaah!!

Pang and Ricky screamed.

Just then, Oliver found
the golden rock covered
with a pile of leaves.

The rock was stuck deep in the ground,
so everyone had to
work together to pull it out.

Finally, they had the last material
to make the glowing ball.

Shasha poured the gold powder into the machine.

Thump!

But when Pang saw the ball,
he was disappointed that it looked
nothing like the one from his dream.

**"It needs to be dark for
the ball to glow!"**
said Shasha.

It was dark and cloudy outside.
Everyone was waiting for the ball to glow.
"I guess today is not the day.
Let's try again tomorrow!" said Shasha.

A little disappointed, Pang tossed the ball into the air.

Just then the clouds cleared up
and the moonlight hit the ball
and it started to glow.

Everyone cheered.

Soon everyone could enjoy a game of cricket at night just like they had in Pang's dream.

The **Cricket Pang** series is a set of picture books with charming stories based on lovable animal characters. The overall theme of the books is cricket, which besides being a very popular sport for children, also lends a unique flavour to this series. Children will love the main character, Pang, and his bunch of friends. Each book highlights important values through engaging stories and endearing characters. With their simple vocabulary and sentence structure, these books are perfect for early readers.

Being fair!

Being fun!

Being kind!

Being smart!

Follow our **YouTube Channel [CricketPang TV]** for more Cricket Pang content.
(QR code on the back cover)